VLAD DRACULA
# DEAD ✠ SOULS
ERZSÉBET BÁTHORY
# RESURRECTION

Written by Kurt Amacker
Illustrated by Montgomery Borror
Finishes by Drake Mefestta and Travis Hymel
Front Cover by Dan Brereton
Back Cover by J.C. Grande
Introduction by Dani Filth

"Behold I teach you the overman. The overman is the meaning of the earth. Let your will say: the overman *shall be* the meaning of the earth! I beseech you, my brothers, *remain faithful to the earth*, and do not believe those who speak to you of otherworldly hopes!"
~Friedrich Nietzsche, *Thus Spake Zarathustra*

DARK NOTES PRESS
New Orleans, Louisiana

# COPYRIGHTS AND PERMISSIONS

© 2020 - Dark Notes Press, LLC - First Printing - February 2020
All rights reserved under Pan American and International
Copyright Conventions. Republication or reproduction of any of
the included material is strictly prohibited.
International Standard Book Number (ISBN13) - 978-0-9915712-9-1
Published in the United States of America by
Dark Notes Press P.O. Box 740999 New Orleans, LA 70174-0999
www.KurtAmacker.com
www.DarkNotesPress.com

DARK NOTES PRESS

# RESURRECTING DEAD SOULS

## By Dani Filth

I FIRST MET Kurt Amacker in 2007 at a signing in New Orleans, on the Cradle of Filth/69 Eyes/ 3 Inches of Blood tour, and was immediately impressed by his vigour and dedication to the development of his hideous mutant child—the horror comic *Dead Souls*, a bayou-based creepy, featuring not one, but two of the most popular historic horror icons—Vlad Dracula and Erzsébet Bathory—known to modern man. And the era wasn't the late Middle Ages. It was modern day and on first glance it reeked of a dark *Miami Vice* in parts, which I thought was a good thing.

Our brief email liaison continued right up until the first copy (of what turned out to be a three-parter or what we call in monsterland "a thrillogy") fell through my door and gave me a toilet-rim-shaped sore around the back of my thighs, subject to me sitting and reading it start to finish on the lavatory. Again, a good thing—if you forget the sore.

I even contributed an interview to the first issue, one that was conducted by cell phone against a backdrop of bleating sheep, as I was making conversation from a studio that was on a farm at the time. Had he heard (and now knowing Kurt), I'm sure he would've attributed the bleating to the restless, murdered spirits of the underworld, or the stirring of ghouls, or something equally nightmarish. He certainly is creative and quite possibly nuts. This is a good thing in this line of work!

This continued "fiendship," if you will, led me to Kurt's own virtual doorstep in 2013, when I asked him if he'd lend his poison pen to Cradle of Filth's own comic book cryptid. The end result, *The Curse of Venus Aversa*, featured our mutual plotting, with his script, and the art of one Montgomery Borror (whom we lovingly called "Monty the Borrible" during the book's creation). It was a Victorian nightmare down a rabbithole of references to Poe, Stoker, bits of horrifying history, and Cradle's own lyrical excretions. It was a resounding success thanks to all of the fans who threw in on a Kickstarter campaign, and we got to tell exactly the story we wanted. Now, Monty has returned here with Kurt for this newly-drawn and expanded edition of the original story. This very graphic novel has matured the story from a supernatural detective yarn into the post-millennial world of competing law enforcement agencies, shadowy security contractors, and the ghosts and villains of history returning to haunt the present. There is also a stirring dose of real-world horror, with a new subplot involving the human trafficking victims en route from Cambodia to New Orleans.

But when we conducted our interview for the first issue of *Dead Souls* in 2008, Kurt asked about my interest (and his, or indeed, anybody's interest) in these bloodthirsty villains from the past.

I have always been fascinated with monsters, werewolves, and demons. They have pervaded my entire life. I have an affinity for folklore, castles, and spectres. In fact, when I lived in the historic market town of Hadleigh, Suffolk, England, I rented a house that once also roofed the Witchfinder General Matthew Hopkins, and, certainly, on numerous occasions my wife and I were witness to ghosts. And from an early age, post dinosaur-obsession to be sure, I have held a very high interest in all aspects of the occult, even lending what precious little knowledge I have of it to a book entitled *The Gospel of Filth*—a decadent occult bible of which I was a co-conspirator with journalist Gavin Baddeley. The band I front and my current day job (for the last twenty-eight odd years in fact—odd being the definitive word) is, of course, Cradle of Filth; a bombastic, symphonic metal horror show whose albums have been infused with classical occult flavourings since day zero, dedicating at least four full concept records to the stories of Lucifer, Lilith, Gilles De Rais, and Erzsébet Bathory, respectively.

That kind of brings me full mystic-circle round to why I'm equipped to prattle on about her in these unhallowed pages. On the other hand, Vlad Dracula is a powerful archetype for any band whose monicker screams "Supreme Vampyric Evil," and whose debut album, *The Principle of Evil Made Flesh*, boasts a gorgeous photo of two naked Sapphic beauties adrift in the throes of vampiric orgasm. Indeed, the theme of vampirism and inherent bloodlust pervades even our lattermost musical excretions. But for the best part of one year in particular, it saturated everything.

It was the latter half (the magical, colourful, festive half) of 1997, and we, as a band, were writing the music toward (what then became) *Cruelty and the Beast*, our musical reworking of the life of Erzsébet Bathory. Struggling as I was to hang a story about the bones of the album and with my mind beginning to stray to visuals, I was suddenly seized by the very Gothic and fairytale image of Countess Bathory, reclining naked by candlelight in her tottering tower room, splashed with the blood of her latest plaything, perched as her castle was between phallic snowy peaks. At least that's how I saw it in my head, where the cotton candy lives. And, from that moment forth, I was possessed by Erzsébet body and soul, right up until the album was toured, bled, and put to eventual death. I hung the infamous portrait of the austere-looking Countess in my office, I read everything known to the printed word about her and then set to work on a Gothic fairytale flight of fancy—our own retelling of her story, with further morbid cause and consequence.

We even drafted in the exquisitely beautiful Ingrid Pitt, who'd made the role of Bathory her own in the 1971 Hammer horror movie *Countess Dracula* (and who sadly died just before her 73rd birthday in 2010), to authenticate the deal, which she delivered with her usual whirlwind thespian gusto. Such was that year tied to the service of the Countess and yet, even now, with more and more interest being paid to her life and legend nigh twenty years on, Cradle of Filth are still name-checked in and around the same breath, which is...well, rather nice. I should add here that I spent much of the previous month at Grindstone Studios here in Suffolk, working with producer Scott Atkins on what we have dubbed an "anatomical remix" for the (late) twentieth anniversary of *Cruelty and the Beast*. Available now!

Regardless, what grabbed me from the off about the original *Dead Souls* was the notion of setting it in modern New Orleans, with both Vlad and Erzsébet questioning their immortality, each as eager to break the undecidedness of their situation as the other and to unravel the mysteries of reason and purpose. Why were they immortal? Why them? They had both been monsters for sure, but the real grit was that there were no true answers, with ample deliberation on the presence of God. The chapter breaks of this new edition drive home the existential madness of the story, peppered with quotes from Nietzsche, Camus, Sartre, and the like. It's like someone locked a philosopher in a coffin with Tom Clancy and a rabid bat!

Then there is also the moral issue of the story to consider, the fact that these people who have known violence and bloodshed in life are doomed to repeat their mistakes even with the "gift" of immortality. For there's the rub—the reason we as readers are drawn to stories such as this (not unlike the proverbial deathshead to a flame) is the lure of the bloodthirsty anti-hero—the grinning Dexter, the charming royal vampire, the midnight vigilante, the Dark Lord of the Sith...at least something or someone to put the face of evil to. We want someone other than that dreadful beast in the mirror. And chances are we eventually grow to sympathize with these characters, even finding similarities between their situations, however terrible, and our own often mundane existence. We find ourselves hoping for their eventual redemption, just as we hope for own.

In truth, in *Dead Souls*, the true progenitors of evil are the degenerate cabal of corrupt police officers, and what was originally the arch-villain supergroup Ragnarok, here refashioned as a Cobra-esque security contractor called Deadbolt. Erzsébet and Vlad almost pale in comparison to these power-crazed creatures as together they discover fresh purpose to their destiny and right a few wrongs along the way. And compared to those two, I'm practically a saint (Germain).

Anyhoo, that's about it from my candlelit quill. A nice hot bloodbath and then a snug mildew-free coffin awaits. I'd quickly like to thank God, my manager, my hair stylist, teeth file-ist, and, of course, Kurt Amacker, for inviting me into his pantheon and allowing me my ten penneth worth of drivel here. I'm sure we haven't heard the last from the *Dead Souls* mythos, at any stretch. What was once a supernatural detective story that was charming in its rawness is now a much more mature work of 21st century political Gothic (to coin a subgenre). Thus it's my pleasure to leave you dwelling on it's monumental cliffhanger that even Flash Gordon would be proud of, fizzing away in his silver bottle rocket. It is the unveiling of the face of evil—but what's even more interesting is what's to be done with it.

DANI FILTH
*Midian, Suffolk*
*December 2019*

# WITH DEEPEST THANKS

## By Kurt Amacker

THE JOURNEY TO resurrect *Dead Souls* has been one fraught with delays and controversy. I abandoned the earlier effort to simply collect the first three issues of the miniseries, as published by Seraphemera Books from 2008 through 2010. Though I am grateful for the positive response to the original series, I was never truly happy with it. This new volume is nothing less than a remake. Some of the original script remains. The old art was also used as a starting point for Monty Borror to recreate the entire story with my copious notes and changes. Monty was, to say the least, incredibly patient. He was instrumental in rebuilding the story from the worthwhile pieces of the original series and the new ones that I envisioned. There are new subplots, more developed characters, and a more detailed treatment of the historical record. But this is a work of fiction. Liberties are taken from time to time. Regardless, I've always felt like Vlad, Erzsébet, and St. Germain were worth revisiting.

I began writing the script for the first issue of *Dead Souls* in 2003 in a barracks room in Camp Pendleton, California. My reserve unit in the Marines had been activated for the coming war in Iraq. I had just finished my undergraduate degree with an eye to join the New Orleans Police Department, but we were called up and sent to Twenty-Nine Palms. As fate would have it, I fell out of a low window in MOUT (Military Operations in Urban Terrain) training and dislocated my left knee. It had remained wobbly after catastrophically losing my first-ever boxing match at a reserve drill the year before. After the fall of Baghdad, my company departed for Al-Kūt to conduct security operations. Anyone with an injury was remanded to Camp Pendleton for long-term recovery.

I would never compare my time in California to those of my compatriots in Iraq. Thankfully, no one in my unit was killed. While they reestablished civil order in Al-Kūt, I was left to undergo physical therapy and surgery. I was tasked with various odd jobs. But, in the evenings, I began to write the script for the first issue of *Dead Souls* on a yellow legal pad. I'd already jotted the initial idea on scraps of receipt paper while working as a drugstore security guard six months prior. It was a similar premise of Vlad Dracula and Erzsébet Bathory as vigilantes, wrapped up in some sort of Catholic horror conspiracy. At one point it was to be a pitch for Marvel's failed take-all-comers Epic imprint, and then it was to be a novel. In 2003, a poorly received horror film called *The Order* starring Heath Ledger showed in theaters. The premise was largely the same as my own. I was annoyed, to say the least. Ledger would later shine as the Joker in *The Dark Knight* before his untimely death, but my original idea would only see the inside of a trashcan. It was probably for the best.

I began a new script with a simple premise and no idea where it would end. The historical versions of Vlad Dracula and Erzsébet Bathory would meet in New Orleans. They would be immortal, but they were not vampires. The mystery of their resurrection and immortality would drive the narrative. And because it was a comic book, they would kill criminals. Where the script went after was a matter of inspiration, logistics, and practicality.

But what of Cradle of Filth?

Long before Dani Filth asked me to co-author the band's graphic novel, *The Curse of Venus Aversa* in 2013, a fellow student named Ashley had introduced me to the band and black metal in general. This was my senior year of college, and another friend also lent me the book *Lords of Chaos* by Michael Moynihan and Didrik Søderlind. I realize their journalistic foray into the Scandinavian black metal scene is controversial, as is Cradle of Filth's place in that pantheon. Initially, I couldn't make the leap from my beloved moody Gothic and post-punk baritones, (think Joy Division, Bauhaus, and The Sisters of Mercy) to this incomprehensible screaming. But, between that semester and my time recovering in a barracks room, I had assembled a collection of albums by Darkthrone, Emperor, Ulver, Mayhem, and a few other luminaries whose names I won't print in a semi-respectable publication. Cradle of Filth's *Cruelty and the Beast* had helped me to make the leap. It made me understand not just the band, but the fiendish reverence for myth and history embodied in black metal.

Their narrative rendition of the crimes of Erzsébet Bathory immediately fascinated me. The album not only helped me to understand the genre, but reignited a long-dormant desire to explore the darkerst corners of history. I started with Raymond McNally's *Dracula Was a Woman* (1983), which served as his de facto follow-up to *In Search of Dracula*, which was his 1974 exposé about Vlad the Impaler that he co-authored with Radu Florescu. That volume alerted much of the Western media to the "real Dracula." While their book was a noble effort for the time, the Countess's story has since been explored and explained more thoroughly by Tony Thorne in

Filth and *Cruelty and the Beast* reawakened my love of history and literature. You might call it the right time and the right place. But something was set into motion that I could not quite explain. There began my journey. I even visited the Bathory castle in Čachtice, Slovakia in 2016. Some would argue this volume is only one step along the way in that journey.

I returned to New Orleans in 2004 after an honorable discharge. In 2007, after the first issue of *Dead Souls* was roughly completed, I found a publisher in Marc Moorash of Seraphemera Books. Both of us had the shared experience of working on comics, while also promoting Goth club events in our respective cities. After reaching out to Dani Filth through his then-label Roadrunner Records for a supplementary interview, the first issue launched in the summer of 2008. Despite its rawness, it received a surprisingly positive reception. By the time the second issue was published the next year, I'd asked Alan Moore to provide a cover quote. I'd met him over the phone while writing editorial content for the now defunct *Cinescape*, and we'd kept in touch. He liked the comic, and understood how much support his voice might lend. In 2010, I said good-bye to the series with a concert featuring the industrial band Android Lust, with my friend's band Suicide Assyst opening. I realized that some of the audience was undoubtedly there just for the music, but *Dead Souls* had developed a small cult following along the Gulf Coast. The turnout blew me away. I even did a reading in front of the crowded, drunken bar before Shikhee D'iordna took the stage. For a black and white underground comic, it had gathered an impressive fanbase.

I immediately began thinking about the future. I always thought to collect the original three issues, but to have a new artist take a pass at the book. When this failed (repeatedly), I abandoned the process and decided to recreate the story. I launched a Kickstarter after the successful crowdfunding of *Cradle of Filth: The Curse of Venus Aversa*. But, before the campaign ended, I realized that the project would never get off the ground as such. I canceled it, but it was for the best. Backers might still be waiting for their orders. With a PDF of the original book, I made copious notes for Monty. I realized that both the horrors of the Soviet Union and modern human trafficking required a more detailed treatment. As such, the flashbacks are longer. And a new character has been added in Davy Chanda—a Khmer girl who has been taken by the slavers. While *Dead Souls* has always been an action story, I always intended it to convey more than cheap thrills . The chapter pages (at least in the American, printed version) are accented with epigraphs from existentialist writers, which illustrate Vlad's spiritual journey. I wanted to emphasize the story's philosophical overtones as much as its cinematic and comic influences. The story of resurrected dictators has been done in *The Boys from Brazil* and *Archangel*. And, yes, the idea of wandering immortals has more than a little *Highlander* in it. What I wanted most, though, was for *Dead Souls* to embrace the trappings of both the 1980s action films and Bronze Age comics that influenced it, and to renew them with a contemplative, inquisitive perspective. Monty's art takes a healthy dose of influence from both Gene Colan and Bernie Wrightson. The story also leans heavily on narrative captions, creating a sense that the script is almost larger than the book can contain—all familiar tropes to anyone who grew up loving comics written by Marv Wolfman, Doug Moench, and Larry Hama. And, of course, there is the obvious influence of 1980s and '90s underground comics. James O'Barr's *The Crow* is the most prominent example, but it grew out of the same era of Hart Fisher's Boneyard Press and Mirage Studios' early *Teenage Mutant Ninja Turtles*. There was a time when comics had a sense of danger to them. In an era where you can see anything online, that seems quaint. But I've always missed the feeling that the medium could be seedy and disreputable—almost to the point of being out of control.

All of the interviews and editorial content from the original trilogy have been preserved here, along with a short story called "An Immortal Interlude" with art by Ben "1314" Hansen, who drew one of the segments in *The 69 Eyes: Helsinki Vampires*. The story was part of an anthology which has long been out of print. With that, I'd like to thank you most of all, dear reader, for waiting patiently for this volume, and, in no particular order:

The Amacker Family, the Funderburk Family, the United States Marine Corps, Graham Hayes, Laura Duvall, Lisa Andresen, Kimberly and Brian Hirsius, Drake Mefestta, Dani Filth and Cradle of Filth, Jyrki 69 and The 69 Eyes, Valor and Maitri and Christian Death, Aurelio Voltaire, Alan Moore and Melinda Gebbie, Ashley Sieffert Martinez, Amy Sciarretto, Alica Smith, M. Damien Regnard et Mme. Bertille Regnard, Maven Lore, Lord Chaz, Tim Peterson, Dan Chiorean, Tripp Frasch, Tami Monk and Fear Fete, Danny and Anne Marie Harvey, Derec Donovan, Tim Lattie, Fletch Boogie, Travis Hymel, Shades Casanova and Shadow Reborn, Michael Gunn, Cindy Richardson, Mange Voorhees, Destiny Maddox, Lisa KyDuyen Tran, Katie Picone, Amanda Howard, Holly Taylor, Marc Moorash and Ava Dawn Heydt at Seraphemera Books, Brad Richard, Anne Gisleson, Richmond Eustis, Blake Bailey, Jim Fitzmorris, Clare Marie Nemanich, and all of the Southern con organizers for tolerating me. Finally, I wish to thank my wife, Sabrina, without whom none of this would be possible.

# EXPERIENCE 1: REAWAKENING

"When Gregor Samsa woke one morning from troubled dreams, he found himself transformed right there in his bed into some sort of monstrous insect."

~Franz Kafka, *The Metamorphosis*

--A WOMAN SO VAIN THAT SHE BATHED IN THE BLOOD OF VIRGINS TO REMAIN YOUNG. SHE WAS IMPRISONED WITHOUT TRIAL BY THE HUNGARIAN CROWN IN 1611, AFTER HER SERVANTS WERE TRIED AND TORTURED ON HER BEHALF.

MUCH OF MY TIME IS SPENT READING AND RESEARCHING MY CONDITION--AND SEARCHING FOR OTHERS.

ERZSÉBET BÁTHORY--THE BLOOD COUNTESS OF CÁCHTICE--

"ELIZABETH, WASHED IN THAT DEADLY BATH, APPEARED TO HERSELF YET MORE BEAUTIFUL, UNDER NO OTHER INFLUENCE, NO ONE WILL DOUBT...

"...THAN DIABOLIC MOCKERY.

"THIS FIRST CRIME, BORN OF HER WILLFULNESS...

"...RENDERED HER MORE COURAGEOUS.

"THE WICKED DEEDS WENT ON YEAR AFTER YEAR...

"...AND, YOU WILL BE ASTONISHED TO LEARN, EVEN AFTER THE DEATH OF HER HUSBAND...

"...THE WIDOW, NOW ADVANCING IN YEARS...

"...WAS RESPONSIBLE FOR A SACRILEGIOUS SHEDDING OF BLOOD." --"A SHORT DESCRIPTION OF HUNGARY, TOGETHER WITH ITS KINGS" BY FATHER LASZLO TUROCZI, 1744.

WHEN THE LEGENDS OF MY OWN LAND PROVED GROUNDLESS, I CAME TO NEW ORLEANS. THE CITY BREATHES WITH TALES OF VAMPIRES, VOODOO, AND RESTLESS SPIRITS.

WITH REASON EXHAUSTED, I TURNED TO THE SUPER-NATURAL. I THOUGHT THAT, PERHAPS BURIED IN FOLKLORE, I MIGHT FIND TRUTH--THAT I MIGHT UNDERSTAND THIS THING THAT I HAVE BECOME.

INSTEAD, I FOUND ONLY CHEAP HORROR STORIES SOLD TO TOURISTS AND MYTHOLOGY SCRAWLED ACROSS THE PAGES OF HISTORY.

THE RAZOR'S EDGE REMINDS ME THAT...

...I AM FOREVER ALIVE...

...IN BODY...

...AND NOTHING MORE.

MY GOD, WHAT HAVE I REDUCED MYSELF TO?

IT HEALS ALMOST INSTANTLY, AS IT HAS SO MANY TIMES BEFORE.

IT CANNOT BE HER, AND SHE WILL NOT BE AS I AM--JUST LIKE ALL THE OTHERS BEFORE.

I AM ALONE.

MY NAME IS VLAD III.

HISTORY REMEMBERS ME AS *DRACULA*-- SON OF VLAD II DRACUL OF THE NOBLE ORDER OF THE DRAGON.

IN FEAR OF MY WILL AND MY WAYS AS VOIVODE OF WALLACHIA, THEY CALLED ME "TEPES"--*THE IMPALER*

LEGENDS OF MY CRUELTY SPREAD EVEN IN MY OWN LIFETIME.

1140 ROYAL STREET-- THE NEXT DAY...

IN 1834, DELPHINE LALAURIE AND HER HUSBAND FLED THIS HOUSE AND THE CITY WITH AN ANGRY MOB AT THEIR BACKS. THE AUTHORITIES HAD RESPONDED TO A KITCHEN FIRE, BUT THEY DISCOVERED SOMETHING FAR MORE TERRIBLE.

A SLAVE HAD STARTED THE BLAZE, EVEN AS SHE WAS CHAINED TO THE STOVE. SHE WANTED THE MEN TO FIND THE ATTIC. THE LALAURIES HAD TORTURED THEIR SLAVES FOR YEARS, IMPRISONING THEM THERE IN THE HEAT AND THE DARKNESS.

ACCOUNTS OF THE INCIDENT VARY, AND I TRUST FEW OF THEM.

IT SEEMS APPROPRIATE, THOUGH, THAT *SHE* WOULD PICK THIS HOUSE.

SHE WOULD FEEL AT HOME WITH THE MEMORIES OF THE DEAD...

...KNOWING ALL THAT THEY HAD SUFFERED.

BZZT!

YES?

I HAVE A PACKAGE TO DELIVER.

BE RIGHT DOWN.

GLAD YOU'RE FINALLY HERE. WE'VE BEEN--

YOU DON'T LOOK LIKE A DELIVERY GUY.

I AM AFRAID THAT I LIED.

I AM HERE TO SEE, AH, "MISTRESS ANASATZIA."

MISTRESS ISN'T IN RIGHT NOW.

AND, UNLESS YOU HAVE AN APPOINTMENT--

--WHICH, BY THE WAY, I KNOW YOU DON'T--

--SHE WON'T SEE YOU.

SO, WHY DON'T YOU JUST--

SHIT!

YOU WILL TAKE ME TO YOUR MISTRESS NOW.

I WILL *NOT* BE DISMISSED BY A *SERVANT*.

WHAT IS IT THAT YOU WANT?

JUST TO TALK.

YOU HAVE SAID THAT ALREADY.

IS IT MONEY?

NO.

WOULD YOU AT LEAST TELL ME WHO YOU ARE?

LOOK CLOSELY.

LISTEN, I DO NOT--

I DIED ALMOST ONE HUNDRED YEARS BEFORE YOU WERE BORN.

HOLY SHIT!

DRACULA! OR PRINCE VLAD, I GUESS.

"VLAD" WILL BE FINE. I HAVE NOT BEEN A PRINCE FOR MANY YEARS.

THEN YOU ARE IMMORTAL TOO?

CHRIST, OF COURSE YOU ARE. I AM SORRY.

I JUST NEVER EXPECTED THIS.

REGARDLESS, I DO NOT KNOW WHAT WE ARE, OR HOW WE ARE EVEN ALIVE.

DO YOU?

NO, VLAD. I DO NOT.

I DIED ALONE IN A CELL WITHOUT A TRIAL.

THEN, I WOKE UP SUDDENLY.

AND I COULD NOT DIE.

I ALWAYS BELIEVED THAT I WAS THE ONLY ONE.

I HAVE YET TO MEET OTHERS--AND I HAVE SEARCHED FOR YEARS.

BUT IF THERE ARE TWO, THEN THERE ARE LIKELY EVEN MORE.

*SIGH* THIS IS ALL VERY TRYING.

SO, NOW THAT YOU HAVE FOUND ME, WHAT IS IT THAT YOU WANT FROM ME?

I HAVE A... *PROPOSITION* OF SORTS FOR YOU.

FIRST, TELL ME WHY YOU ARE HERE.

HERE? WHAT DO YOU MEAN?

I WANTED THIS HOUSE FOR ITS HISTORY.

DELPHINE LALAURIE...SHE JUST REMINDS ME SO MUCH--

WHY DID YOU LEAVE EUROPE?

WELL...

...MY HUSBAND DIED.

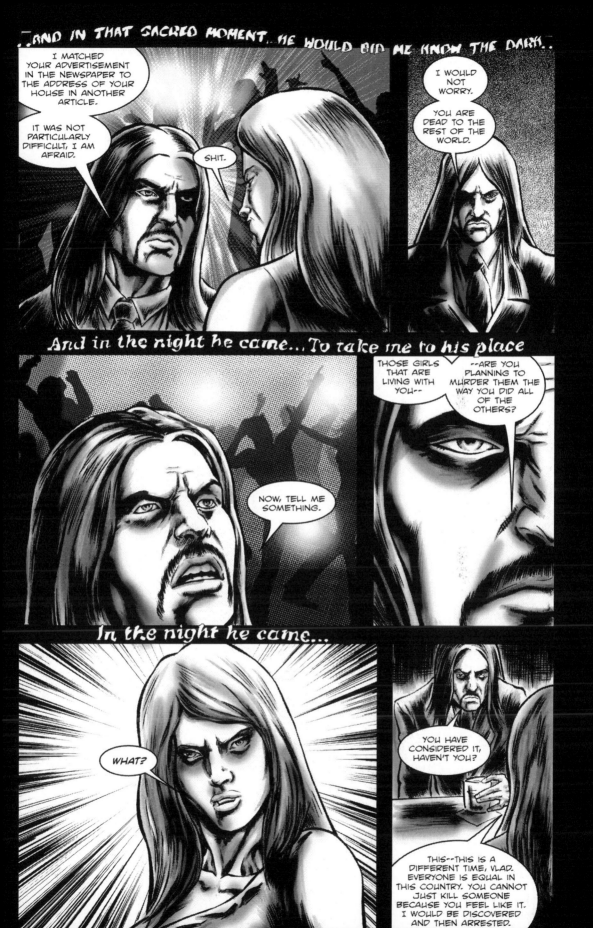

# EXPERIENCE II:REEMERGENCE

"The great epochs of our life come when we gain
the courage to rechristen our evil as what is best
in us."
~Friedrich Nietzsche, *Beyond Good and Evil*

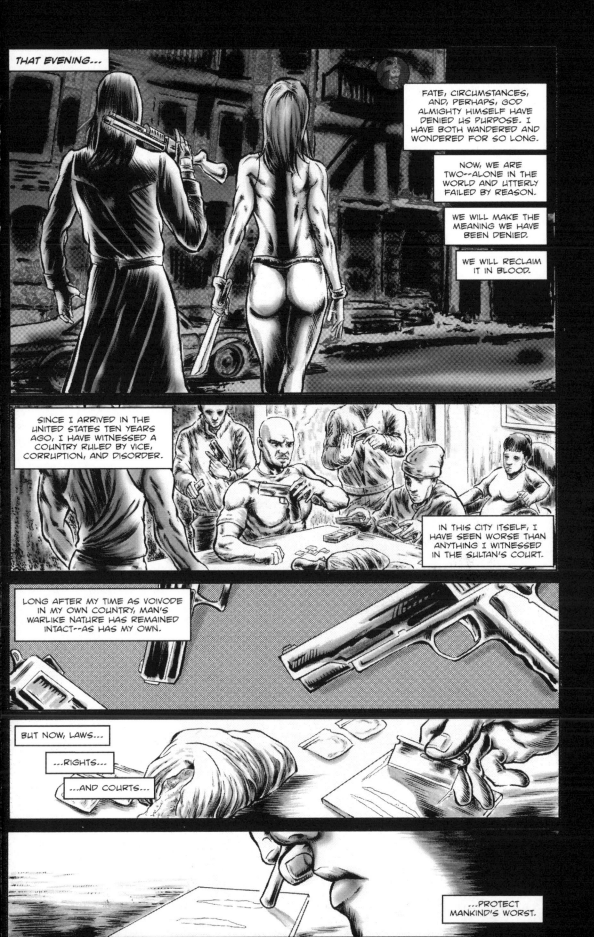

"SHIT. LET ME GUESS: THE FEDS SHOWED UP?"

"I DON'T REALLY KNOW WHO THEY WERE. THEY DIDN'T ACTUALLY SAY."

UA-ROOMMM!

"WAIT. THEY DIDN'T?"

"MARK, BABY, I'VE TALKED TO THE F.B.I. BEFORE, AND USUALLY THEY'RE ALL 'YES MA'AM, NO MA'AM.' YOU KNOW WHAT I'M SAYIN'? THESE GUYS WERE MORE LIKE..."

"...MEN IN BLACK."

...NOW, KINDLY *VACATE* MY CRIME SCENE.

"ONE OF THEM A TALL BLACK GUY? PERMA-NENTLY PISSED OFF?"

YOU EVER HEARD OF THE FIRST AMEND-MENT?

GIVE ME BACK MY CAMERA!

"YEAH. YOU KNOW HIM? SHOULD I HAVE SAID 'HELLO'?"

GET THEM OUT OF HERE, *NOW.*

YOU KNOW WHAT TO DO.

WEIRD THEY DIDN'T ACTUALLY ARREST Y'ALL.

NO, THEY JUST RAN US OFF.

SO, YOU DID THE STORY ANYWAY?

WELL, OBVIOUSLY.

# EXPERIENCE III: REVELATION

"Open the door! Open, blast you! I'll endure anything, your red-hot tongs and molten lead, your
racks and prongs and garrotes—all your fiendish
gadgets, everything that burns and flays and tears
—I'll put up with any torture you impose.
Anything, anything would be better than this agony
of mind, this creeping pain that gnaws and fumbles
and caresses one and never hurts quite enough."
~Jean-Paul Sartre, *No Exit*

ARE YOU ALL RIGHT, DARLING?
HUFF...HUFF... WHO ARE YOU?
SOMETHING IN THE ROUNDS...
...BURNS...WOUNDS...
...NOT HEALING.
ARE WE...
...DYING?
VLAD...
...HUH-- HELP...
...ME.
I... CAN'T.

WAIT.

DON'T MOVE.

SQUINCH

ARGH!

OH, FOR CHRIST'S SAKE. WILL YOU PLEASE SHUT UP?

I'VE ALREADY REMOVED IT.

YOU KNOW...

TINK!

...YOU REALLY AREN'T LIVING UP TO YOUR REPUTATION.

WHO...WHO ARE YOU?

THE ONLY ONE WHO CAN HELP YOU.

NOW...

VLAD... HE'S--

...HOLD STILL, YOU OLD BITCH.

AÄÄAAAIIIEEE!

CLOP
CLOP
CLOP
CLOP

MONSIEUR DE RAIS! HOW ARE YOU FEELING TODAY?

<I HAVE ALREADY CONFESSED AND BEGGED FOR GOD'S FORGIVENESS!>

<PLEASE, SIR...JUST LET ME DIE!>*

*TRANSLATED FROM FRENCH

YOU WILL FIND MY FRENCH, LACKING, MY FRIEND.

IT TOOK ME LONG ENOUGH TO LEARN ENGLISH.

PERHAPS YOU CAN TEACH ME SOME DAY.

GENERAL STALIN!

CLACK!

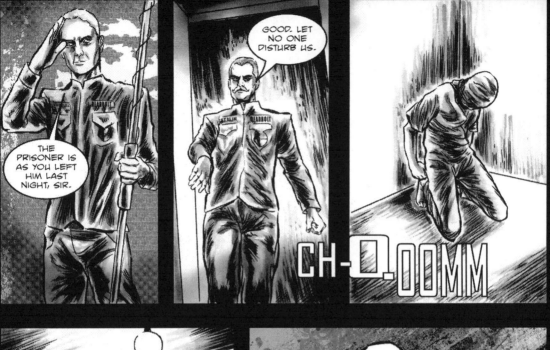

"I HAD SPENT MOST OF MY YEARS AS A MAN HEADLONG IN DRINKING, WHORING, AND GAMBLING. I HAD SURVIVED A LIFE OF INDULGENCE. BUT NOW, AS I WAITED IN THAT CAVE, I HOPED THAT NATURE WOULD DO WHAT I LACKED THE COURAGE TO.

"I HUDDLED THERE IN THE DARKNESS, WHISPERING TO THE BITTER ENGLISH WINTER.

"'TAKE ME,' I RASPED BETWEEN SOBS.

"I LOST ALL SENSE OF TIME AS I DRIFTED IN AND OUT OF SLEEP, HOPING NEVER TO AWAKE.

"THEN, I SAW A LIGHT FLICKERING FROM THE DEPTHS OF THE CAVERN.

"NEARLY BLINDED, I CRAWLED TOWARDS THE ILLUMINATION.

"AT ITS CENTER, THERE SAT AN OBJECT I FELT SURE HAD BEEN FORGED IN HEAVEN ITSELF.

"THE SIGHT OF IT NEARLY OVER-WHELMED ME. I ALMOST FLED DEEPER INTO THE CAVE.

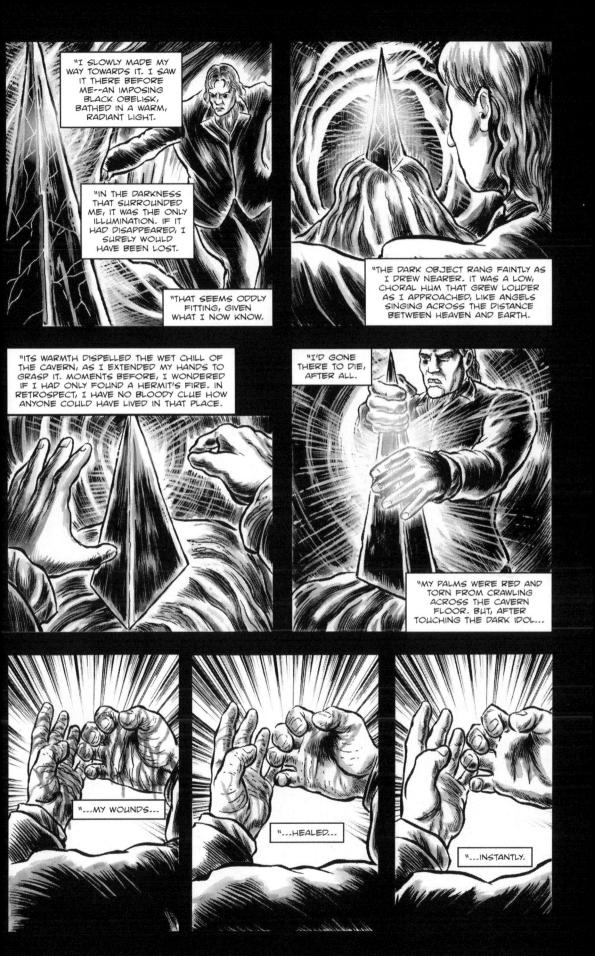

"I FELT SURE THAT GOD HIMSELF HAD INTERVENED IN MY SUICIDE. ONLY HOURS BEFORE, I HAD RESOLVED TO DIE. BUT I KNEW THEN THAT I WAS MEANT FOR SOMETHING GREATER.

"I RAN FROM THE CAVE WITH THE BLACK STONE IN HAND. ITS ILLUMINATION GUIDED ME TO THE CAVERN'S ENTRANCE.

"I HAD A NOTION OF WHAT I'D FOUND, BUT I RETURNED TO MY LODGINGS TO MAKE CERTAIN.

"I GATHERED A PILE OF METAL OBJECTS--BELT BUCKLES, KEYS, AND A FEW OTHER WORTH-LESS BAUBLES FROM AROUND MY ROOM.

"I HELD A SINGLE BREATH AND STEADIED MY HAND, WITH A BUCKLE CLENCHED IN MY WAITING FINGERS.

"I PRESSED IT AGAINST THE SIDE OF THE OBELISK. THERE--WITH NO ONE BUT GOD ABOVE TO BEAR WITNESS --MY SUSPICIONS WERE CONFIRMED.

"THE SIMPLE PIECE OF BRASS-- WORTH NO MORE THAN A COIN OR TWO--TRANSFORMED INTO *GOLD.*

"I'D READ OF THE *PHILOSOPHER'S STONE* IN MY YOUTH, IN THE WORKS OF THE ARAB ALCHEMIST ABU MUSA JABIR IBN HAYYAN. HE'D DESCRIBED THE STONE AS AN ELEMENT UNTO ITSELF. NO ONE EVER THOUGHT THAT IT MIGHT'VE BEEN A SINGLE ARTIFACT.

"IT WAS A GIFT SENT BY ALMIGHTY GOD HIMSELF AND GIVEN TO ME.

"I'D WITNESSED THE STONE'S HEALING PROPER- TIES IN THE CAVE EARLIER THAT DAY.

"ANCIENT LORE SPOKE OF THE STONE'S POWER TO BESTOW EVERLASTING LIFE.

"WITHOUT HESITATION, I CHISELED AWAY A SMALL FRAGMENT...

"...AND DRAPED IT ABOUT MY NECK.

"BY WEARING IT, I RETAINED MY YOUTH AND NO HARM COULD BEFALL ME.

"I WAS YOUNG, RICH, AND IMMORTAL.

"I *WAS* MEANT FOR SOMETHING GREATER. BUT THE PHILOSOPHER'S STONE FAILED TO MAKE ME ANY WISER. I IMMEDIATELY RESUMED THE LIFE OF EXCESS I'D TRIED TO ABANDON ONLY HOURS BEFORE."

# RATATA NOOO! TATATA

"A SINGLE SURVIVOR LED A PATROL BACK. NOW BETTER PREPARED, OUR MEN WERE ABLE TO SHACKLE HIM FOR RETURN TO MOSCOW.

<DOES HE SPEAK RUSSIAN?>

<ROMANIAN. BUT HE SEEMS TO UNDERSTAND GERMAN.>

<GOOD. SO DO I.>

<YOU: WHO ARE YOU?>*

<I ALREADY TOLD YOUR MEN. I AM VLAD, PRINCE OF WALLACHIA.>

<WHERE AM I? WHAT YEAR IS THIS?>

<YOU ARE IN MOSCOW, THE CAPITAL OF THE UNION OF SOVIET SOCIALIST REPUBLICS.>

<THE YEAR IS 1940.>

<I WILL ASK YOU AGAIN: WHO ARE YOU, REALLY?>

<I TOLD YOU--->

*TRANSLATED FROM GERMAN

<THERE IS NO MORE WALLACHIA. DRACULA IS DEAD.>

<AND YET, HERE I SIT BEFORE YOU.>

*TRANSLATED FROM RUSSIAN

ONE WEEK LATER...

"I ARRIVED THAT DAY UNSURE OF WHO OR WHAT I MIGHT SEE.

"I SOUGHT AT FIRST ONLY TO BE UNDERSTOOD."

<YOU.>*

*TRANSLATED FROM GERMAN

<THEY SAY YOU SPEAK GERMAN? I SPEAK A LITTLE.>

<YES. DOES NO ONE HERE UNDERSTAND ROMANIAN?>

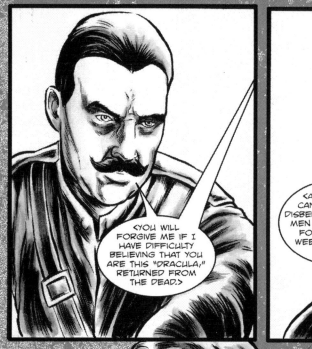

<YOU WILL FORGIVE ME IF I HAVE DIFFICULTY BELIEVING THAT YOU ARE THIS "DRACULA," RETURNED FROM THE DEAD.>

<AND YET YOU CANNOT WHOLLY DISBELIEVE ME. YOUR MEN TORTURED ME FOR AN ENTIRE WEEK, AND HERE I SIT.>

<I SHOULD REMIND YOU THAT I HAVE BEEN IMPRISONED BEFORE. IN TIME, I WILL ESCAPE.>

<THEN, I WILL KILL EVERY MAN IN THIS BUILDING ON MY WAY OUT--ESPECIALLY THAT HULKING BASTARD, SERGEI.>

<AFTER THAT, I WILL SURRENDER MYSELF TO YOUR ENEMIES TO THE WEST AND OFFER MY SERVICES.>

<FINALLY, I WILL HELP THEM BURN YOUR COUNTRY TO ASHES.>

<THE GERMANS? WE HAVE A NONAGGRESSION PACT. YOU WOULD BE RETURNED TO ME.>

<AFTER A LIFETIME OF FIGHTING, DO YOU TRULY WANT ANOTHER WAR?>

# EXPERIENCE IV: REVIVAL

"Faith itself cannot be mediated into the universal, for it is thereby annulled. Faith is this paradox, and the single individual is utterly unable to make himself intelligible to anyone. One may well imagine that the single individual can make himself intelligible to another single individual in the same situation. Such a view would be unthinkable if people in our age did not try in so many ways to sneak slyly into greatness. The one knight of faith cannot help the other at all. Either the single individual himself becomes the knight of faith by assuming the paradox or he never becomes one."

~Søren Kierkegaard, *Fear and Trembling*

&lt;THE GERMANS ARE MOVING THROUGH EASTERN POLAND. THEY'RE FUCKING US, AND WE ARE GOING TO WAR.&gt;

&lt;I CHANGED THE TARGETS. SHOOT THE NAZI BASTARD IN THE HEAD.&gt;

"WITHIN LESS THAN A YEAR, HE SPOKE SUFFICIENT RUSSIAN. AND HE PROVED HIMSELF AN ACCOMPLISHED OFFICER AND A DEVOTED WORKER. HE WAS MY PRIZE--A MAN LOYAL TO HIS ADOPTED COUNTRY WHO LONGED ONLY TO SERVE IN BATTLE. IT SEEMED AS IF HE HAD BEEN BRED FOR WAR.

"IT WAS, OF COURSE, IN JUNE OF 1941--IN THE MIDDLE OF HIS TRAINING--WHEN EVERYTHING CHANGED.

BLAM BLAM BLAM

"HE COULD STAY IN COMBAT FOR DAYS ON END, COMMANDING MEN AND NEVER STOPPING TO EAT OR SLEEP.

MAMAYEV KURGAN, AT THE BATTLE OF STALINGRAD-- SEPTEMBER 14, 1942...

&lt;ANTON! STAY WITH ME! THEY'RE TRYING TO RETAKE THE HILL!&gt;

&lt;FUCKING FRITZ IS NOT GETTING UP HERE AGAIN!&gt;

"THE HORRORS OF WARFARE IN HIS OWN TIME MADE OURS PALE BY COMPARISON.

BLAM

"HE WAS TRULY A SOVIET SUPER-MAN.

KRUNCH

&lt;YOU WOULD LET YAKOV DIE IN THE GERMANS' CAMP JUST TO *SPITE* HIM?&gt;

&lt;I HAVE NO SON.&gt;

&lt;PREMIER...JOSEPH-- AS A BOY, I WAS HELD PRISONER AT THE COURT OF THE SULTAN TO ENSURE MY FATHER'S LOYALTY. WHEN I RETURNED TO WALLACHIA AS A MAN, MY FATHER HAD BEEN ASSASSINATED AND MY OLDER BROTHER BLINDED AND BURIED ALIVE. I TOOK MY REVENGE ON THE MEN WHO KILLED THEM.&gt;

&lt;IF NECESSARY, I WOULD HAVE PURSUED THEM TO THE ENDS OF THE EARTH!&gt;

&lt;PODPOLKOVNIK DRACULA: YOU, A TYRANT WHO TORTURED AND IMPALED YOUR ENEMIES--YOU ARE CONCERNED ABOUT MY SON?!&gt;

&lt;IF YOU CANNOT STAND FOR YOUR OWN FAMILY, THEN YOU ARE NO MAN AND YOU ARE UNFIT TO RULE.&gt;

&lt;LET ME REMIND YOU THAT I FIGHT FOR YOU AT MY PLEASURE. I AM STILL AT LIBERTY TO OFFER MY SERVICES ELSE-WHERE.&gt;

"AFTER THAT, SOMETHING CHANGED IN HIM. HE FOLLOWED ORDERS, BUT HE BECAME COLD. HE NO LONGER TRUSTED ME. WHEN YAKOV WAS SHOT BY THE GUARDS AT SACHSENHAUSEN, NEITHER OF US SPOKE OF IT.

MEANWHILE...

THROUGHOUT THE EIGHTEENTH CENTURY, I TRAVELED THE PALACES OF EUROPE, ENTERTAINING THEIR NOBILITY AND INDULGING.

WITH BOTH IMMORTALITY AND LIMITLESS WEALTH, I COULD LIVE HOWEVER I WISHED.

"I MOVED EFFORTLESSLY FROM ONE COUNTRY TO ANOTHER, ALWAYS BEARING GIFTS AND MAGIC TRICKS TO STAY IN THE GOOD GRACES OF ROYALTY. I WAS A WANDERING MARVEL AND THE TOAST OF MANY A COURT. AND, THOUGH MY IDENTITY OFTEN CHANGED, MY LEGEND GREW IN HUSHED WHISPERS AND TAVERN TALES..."

"...THE UNDYING ALCHEMIST WHO TURNED ORDINARY METALS INTO GOLD.

YOU SING, YOU PLAY THE VIOLIN WONDERFULLY, AND YOU COMPOSE.

BUT YOU ARE MAD, AND NOT VERY SENSIBLE.

I KNOW. ISN'T IT SIMPLY AMAZING?

"I THOUGHT LITTLE OF MY GOOD FORTUNE. THE PHILOSOPHER'S STONE KEPT ME YOUNG, BEAUTIFUL, AND RICH BEYOND ANYTHING I'D EXPERIENCED, EVEN IN MY FORMER LIFE. THROUGHOUT IT ALL, I SIMPLY DIDN'T CARE WHERE IT HAD COME FROM. I JUST ASSUMED THAT GOD HAD SMILED UPON ME.

"BUT IF IT HAD COME FROM THE DEPTHS OF HELL, IT WOULDN'T HAVE MATTERED.

"IT WAS IN PARIS IN THE YEAR 1925 THAT I LEARNED SO MUCH ABOUT THE CHARM THAT I HAD QUIETLY GUARDED FOR OVER TWO HUNDRED YEARS. I HADN'T EVEN BOTHERED ENLISTING IN THE WAR EFFORT AGAINST THE GERMANS. I WAS, FRANKLY, USELESS.

COME WITH US, ENGLISH BOY! PLEEEASE?!

NOT TONIGHT, MY DEAR. I HAVE OTHER PLANS.

"ONE NIGHT IN MAY OF THAT YEAR, AFTER SEEING THE SPECTACULAR REVUE MISTINGUETT AT THE MOULIN ROUGE, I LEFT MY FRIENDS TO PARTAKE IN YET ANOTHER VICE I'D RECENTLY ACQUIRED..."

"...OPIUM.

"MY APPETITES TRULY KNEW NO LIMITS.

"THE PHILOSOPHER'S STONE KEPT ME YOUNG, BUT IT ALSO LEFT ME UTTERLY SOBER.

"BEFORE I CHASED THE DRAGON, I ALWAYS REMOVED THE FRAGMENT FROM AROUND MY NECK.

"PARIS OFFERED AN ENDLESS ARRAY OF INTOXICANTS.

"AFTER TRYING THEM ALL, AND TRYING THEM AGAIN, I'D GROWN LISTLESS AND INDIFFERENT

"I BEGAN TO CONTEMPLATE OBLIVION.

"CARELESS AS I HAD BECOME, IT WAS ONLY A MATTER OF TIME BEFORE SOMEONE DISCOVERED ME.

"HE MUST HAVE COME THROUGH THE WINDOW BEFORE I'D ARRIVED.

WHY WOULD GOD RETURN US TO LIFE, AND THEN SEND *YOU* TO HUNT US DOWN LIKE ANIMALS?

AND WHY DID YOU NOT KILL US?

FAITH IS AN INDIVIDUAL EXPERIENCE, MY FRIEND--A PASSION. I AM BUT A HUMBLE KNIGHT OF FAITH, ANSWERABLE ONLY TO *GOD.*

AND I DIDN'T KILL YOU BECAUSE I NEED YOU FOR SOMETHING.

"ONE OF YOUR BRETHREN HAS BEEN BUSY. AFTER HIS RESURRECTION AROUND 1981..."

"...JOSEPH-FUCKING-STALIN, OF ALL PEOPLE, BEGAN QUIETLY GATHERING SUPPORT ACROSS THE SOVIET UNION. HE'S AMASSED A PRIVATE ARMY. THEY'RE MASQUERADING AS A COMPANY CALLED *DEADBOLT SECURITY SERVICES.*

"THEY'VE A BASE ON OCTOBER REVOLUTION ISLAND, OFF THE COAST OF SIBERIA.

"THEY HAVEN'T GONE PUBLIC YET, BUT THEY PLAN TO OFFER THEIR SERVICES TO ANY GOVERNMENT THAT CAN FOOT THE BILL, AT LEAST INITIALLY.

"THEY'VE MADE INROADS TO SEVERAL LAW ENFORCEMENT AGENCIES IN THE UNITED STATES AND EUROPE, MOSTLY THROUGH BACKCHANNELS. IT ALL *LOOKS* FAIRLY LEGITIMATE FROM THE OUTSIDE. 'FOR A GREATER PEACE' IS HOW THEY ADVERTISE IT ALL.

"BUT THIS WARMER ERA OF AMERICAN-RUSSIAN RELATIONS ISN'T EXACTLY TO JOSEF'S LIKING. THEY WANT THE PHILOSOPHER'S STONE SO THEY CAN MANIPULATE THE WORLD'S ECONOMY. NO ONE WILL REALIZE THAT THE MARKET HAS BEEN FLOODED WITH GOLD UNTIL IT'S TOO LATE.

"IF THE MARKETS ARE CRIPPLED...WELL, JOSEF THINKS HE CAN HAVE ANOTHER SHOT AT HIS *REVOLUTION.*

"THEY'VE GOT EVERYONE WORKING FOR THEM-- MERCENARIES, CORPORATE CRIMINALS OUT ON PAROLE, EX-MAFIA THUGS...ANYBODY WHO'S OFF-GRID.

"ONE OF THEIR AGENTS IS IN NEW ORLEANS RIGHT NOW. BEST I CAN TELL, IT'S AN EX-F.B.I. GUY NAMED HARTFORD. GOT THROWN OUT FOR 'APPROPRIATING' NARCOTICS FROM THE EVIDENCE ROOM AROUND 1994. HE JOINED UP WITH DEADBOLT AFTER.

"THEY ALMOST CAUGHT UP TO YOU THE OTHER NIGHT AFTER YOU BUTCHERED EVERYONE IN THAT HOUSE. HE SAW ME WAITING OUTSIDE, *BUT I SAW HIM FIRST*. I CONNED A COUPLE OF REPORTERS INTO SHOWING UP TO HOLD THEM OFF.

"HARTFORD ARE IN WITH THIS POLICE CAPTAIN NAMED LEWIS. HE'S A GO-BETWEEN FOR THE RUSSIAN MOB. HE AND HIS GUYS ARE BRINGING THE MONEY FOR A BUNCH OF CAMBODIAN GIRLS AT THE PORT. IN EXCHANGE, THEY GET A PERCENTAGE FROM THE LOCAL BRATVA AND ONE NIGHT TO SAMPLE THE MERCHANDISE, AS IT WERE.

WHAT DOES HE WANT IN RETURN?

WELL, THEY DON'T WANT *YOU*, COUNTESS. I'M SORRY TO SAY YOU'RE ONLY HERE BECAUSE VLAD FOUND YOU.

THEY WANT HIM.

LEWIS WANTS JOBS WITH DEADBOLT FOR HIM AND HIS FRIENDS. THEY KNOW IT'S JUST A MATTER OF TIME UNTIL THEY'RE FOUND OUT.

WHAT ABOUT US?

SAN DIEGO INTERNATIONAL AIRPORT--THE NEXT DAY...

THAT'S HER--SARAH WINDSOR. RIGHT ON TIME.

I'VE GOT HER.

WOMENS RESTROOM

SHE JUST WENT INTO THE WOMEN'S ROOM.

I'M ALREADY THERE.

NOW, QUIT TALKING TO ME.

YES OR NO: TWO DAYS AGO, DID SOMEONE PAY YOU IN CASH TO LEAVE THE CITY IMMEDIATELY?

YES. YES, HE DID.

GOOD. NOW, DID YOU WITNESS SOMETHING UNEXPLAINABLE OR SUPERNATURAL BEFORE THAT?

...SUCH AS A PERSON SURVIVING SERIOUS INJURIES, SUCH AS A GUNSHOT WOUND OR APPEARING TO RETURN FROM THE DEAD?

...AND THEN HE AND THIS WOMAN FOUND ME AT THE SAME SPOT, LIKE, A WEEK LATER!

THAT'S WHEN THE BRITISH GUY GAVE ME THE MONEY AND TOLD ME TO LEAVE!

YES... TELL ME MORE ABOUT THE ENGLISHMAN.

I TOLD YOU! HE KILLED THEM!

THAT'S IT! THAT'S ALL I KNOW!

PLEASE DON'T HURT ME.

GOOD. THAT'S WHAT I FIGURED. HOLD ON.

*Beep!!*

HARTFORD SPEAKING.

THIS IS SAN DIEGO.

I JUST HEARD FROM GULPORT. WHAT HAPPENED?

IT'S DONE. ST. GERMAIN IS ALREADY THERE.

I KNOW THAT. WHAT ELSE?

I THINK HE KILLED THE WOMAN AND THE IMPALER.

PLEASE TELL ME YOU'RE JOKING.

DO I EVER JOKE ABOUT ANYTHING?

THAT WAS THE WHOLE REASON WE CAME HERE!

I CAN'T JUST CRAWL BACK TO THE GENERAL AND TELL HIM THAT ST. GERMAIN ALREADY KILLED HIM!

WHAT DOES IT MATTER AS LONG AS HE'S DEAD? KILL ST. GERMAIN, TAKE *THE ARTIFACT*, AND GO BACK TO HEADQUARTERS. THE GENERAL WILL JUST--

*Beep!!*

HE ALREADY KNOWS ABOUT THE ARTIFACT.

IT WON'T MATTER.

HE WANTED TO BE THE ONE TO DO IT.

I'M A DEAD MAN

SALLY'S CORNER BAR--THE NEXT DAY...

ARE YOU SURE NO ONE WILL HEAR US IN HERE?

IT'S HAPPY HOUR ON A FRIDAY. I CAN BARELY HEAR MYSELF. I THINK WE'RE FINE.

AWHAT ARE YOU? YOU BELIEVE YOURSELF TO BE SOME AVATAR OF GOD'S JUSTICE, BUT YOU'VE *KILLED* FOR THE SAME REASON WE HAVE.

ALLOW ME TO GUESS: THE GREATER GOOD? IS THAT IT? THE DIFFERENCE IS THAT I'M WORKING FOR THE HIGHEST GOOD OF ALL.

YOU TWO ARE JUST SADISTS.

IF YOU HAD SEEN THE THINGS THAT I HAVE SEEN, AND LIVED THE LIFE THAT I HAVE--

WILL YOU TWO STOP FUCKING BICKERING?

ST. GERMAIN, WILL YOU PLEASE JUST GET TO THE POINT? WHAT IS IT YOU WANT US TO DO?

YES. YOU SPOKE OF JOSEPH'S COMPANY, *DEADBOLT* AND THE POLICE CAPTAIN'S ARRANGEMENT WITH THE RUSSIANS?

I WANT THE SAME THING YOU'VE WANTED FROM THE START--

--TO KILL A WHOLE LOT OF VERY BAD PEOPLE.

THREE NIGHTS FROM NOW, LEWIS IS HAVING A PARTY.

THAT'S THE ONE NIGHT HE AND HIS MEN GET WITH THE GIRLS BEFORE THE HANDOFF.

HARTFORD AND HIS AGENTS SHOULD BE THERE.

"AS SUCH, SO WILL YOU."

MEANWHILE...

OCTOBER REVOLUTION ISLAND--PART OF THE SEVERNAYA ZEMLYA ARCHIPELAGO--162 MILES NORTHEAST OF THE RUSSIAN MAINLAND...

...FORMER SITE OF THE VAVILOV METEOROLOGICAL STATION, CURRENT HEADQUARTERS OF DEADBOLT

BUZZZZ

CLOP

CLOP

CLOP

# EXPERIENCE V:RECOGNITION

"We wait. We are bored. No, don't protest, we are bored to death, there's no denying it. Good. A diversion comes along and what do we do? We let it go to waste. Come, let's get to work! In an instant all will vanish and we'll be alone once more, in the midst of nothingness!"

~Samuel Beckett, *Waiting for Godot*

"THEY WON'T BE AROUND TO REPORT A DAMN THING."

<I'M SORRY, BUT I DON'T KNOW HOW MUCH LONGER WE'RE GOING TO BE HERE.>*

<BUT WHERE ARE THEY--?>

*TRANSLATED FROM KHMER

<HEY, DAVY.>

<THEY HAVEN'T FED US IN TWO DAYS BECAUSE OF THAT SHIT YOU PULLED.>

<IT'S TIME TO PAY UP, BITCH.>

<VEASNA-- BEAT HER ASS.>

<YOU FUCKING CUNT!>

<I'M GONNA FUCKING--->

<I...;NNG;...I KNEW YOU FOUR WERE UP TO SOMETHING.>

*TRANSLATED FROM KHMER

*TRANSLATED FROM RUSSIAN

# EXPERIENCE VI: REALIZATION

"This universe henceforth without a master seems to him neither sterile nor futile. Each atom of that stone, each mineral flake of that night-filled mountain, in itself forms a world. The struggle itself toward the heights is enough to fill a man's heart. One must imagine Sisyphus happy."

~Albert Camus, *The Myth of Sisyphus*

DEEP IN THE EASTERN END OF NEW ORLEANS...

NOT AS GOOD AS IT USED TO--

CAMBODIA? THOUGHT IT WAS VIETNAM--

LOOK FORWARD TO THIS EVERY YEAR...

SOMEBODY PULLED UP THE LADDER--

YOU KNOW, IN ANCIENT ROME--

ALL RIGHT, GUYS! GATHER 'ROUND! LOOKS LIKE A GOOD CROP THIS YEAR. EVERYBODY'S PAID UP. IF THINGS GO AS PLANNED, THEN...

...WE MIGHT HAVE OUR TICKET OUT OF TOWN!

CLUNK!

DOWN-STAIRS--RADIO CHECK. THEY'RE ABOUT TO BEGIN.

ROGER THAT.

CHRISTIAN, GRAB ALL OF OUR GUYS AND HEAD BACK. THEY'VE GOT ENOUGH GUNS DOWN THERE.

GOT IT. DEADBOLT OUT.

JUST REMEMBER: CELLS, BEEPERS, GUNS, AND BADGES LOCKED UP DOWNSTAIRS. NOBODY'S GETTING ARRESTED TONIGHT--THAT'S FOR SURE.

AND...LET ME CALL ROLL BEFORE WE BEGIN.

THIS IS SO FUCKED UP.

McMASTERS?

HERE!

JACKS?

HERE!

COUNTESS, WATCH THE DOOR!

I DON'T KNOW WHO THE FUCK YOU THINK YOU ARE, BUT--!

I DID NOT KNOW...

KOOM

...UNTIL TONIGHT.

IN A LIFE WITH FEW ANSWERS, WE OFTEN CLING TO THOSE THAT OFFER US THE MOST IN RETURN.

ST. GERMAIN IS MAD. HIS FAITH IS MISGUIDED. BUT HIS MISSION STANDS AGAINST AN EVIL GREATER THAN ANY WE HAVE FOUND ON THE STREETS OF NEW ORLEANS--

--AN EVIL FAR GREATER THAN EVEN OUR OWN.

TO HIM, WE ARE BUT DOGS OF WAR, FIT ONLY TO UNLEASH UPON HIS ENEMIES. WERE WE ANYTHING LESS, WE WOULD HAVE DIED IN THE ALLEY WHERE THIS BEGAN.

CHILDREN-- RUN!

AND, THOUGH WE MAY SHOULDER THAT BURDEN ENDLESSLY, UNTIL THE WORLD'S LAST TWILIGHT, WE WILL DO SO JOYFULLY.

TO DO OTHERWISE MEANS THE DESTRUCTION OF WHAT LITTLE WE HAVE LEFT...

<WHAT DID HE SAY!?>*

<TO RUN!>

*TRANSLATED FROM KHMER

...AND A LIFE FROUGHT WITH GREATER SUFFERING THAN ANY VISION OF HELL.

KOOM

SQUINCH

NO. WE CAN ALL GET OUT OF HERE.

I'M NOT LEAVING WITHOUT YOU.

I KNOW YOU'RE NOT LIKE THE OTHERS.

DAVY...

PLEASE RUN.

RUN!

YOU...YOU'RE SUPPOSED TO BE DEAD. ST. GERMAIN KILLED YOU. IT WAS SUPPOSED TO BE HIM--NOT YOU.

I AM SORRY TO DISAPPOINT YOU.

HE RECRUITED YOU. I SHOULD HAVE GUESSED. HE'D NEVER RISK LOSING THE ARTIFACT LIKE THAT.

SHANNKKT!

NOOO!

I KNOW YOU'RE GOING TO KILL ME. *JUST* LISTEN.

GO! GO! GO!

CAPTAIN NGUYEN! SOME-BODY JUST LIT THIS PLACE UP.

THEY'RE EITHER STILL HERE OR THEY JUST LEFT!

JESUS FUCKING CHRIST.

ALL RIGHT, EVERYBODY UPSTAIRS NOW!

DEADBOLT WILL RULE EVERYTHING ONE DAY, WHETHER ANY OF US LIKES IT OR NOT.

THE GENERAL HAS FOUND... *OTHERS* LIKE YOU.

*TAKE* THE ARTIFACT FROM ST. GERMAIN. GO TO DEADBOLT, AND HE MIGHT--

WOCOWOCOWOO!

URCOOM

CAPTAIN NGUYEN-- THEY'RE ALREADY IN PURSUIT.

GOOD!

YOU'RE THE ONE WHO SPEAKS ENGLISH? FROM THE DOCK?

<NO. I DON'T KNOW WHAT YOU'RE TALKING ABOUT.>*

*TRANSLATED FROM KHMER

I DO NOT KNOW WHY WE HAVE RETURNED.

ST. GERMAIN BELIEVES THAT GOD HAS BOTH CURSED US WITH IMMORTALITY AND SENT HIM TO EXTERMINATE US.

HIS LOGIC IS AS MISGUIDED AS HIS FANATICISM. IF HIS GOD IS REAL, HE RULES WITH NEITHER REASON NOR MERCY.

BUT WHO AM I TO SPEAK OF MERCY?

OVER FIVE HUNDRED YEARS AGO, I THRICE RULED WALLACHIA AT THE POINT OF A SWORD. I THOUGHT MYSELF A WARRIOR AND A PATRIOT. SOME STILL REGARD ME THIS WAY.

I NO LONGER KNOW WHAT MAKES A GOOD LIFE.

I, UH, OKAY--LET'S GET Y'ALL OUT OF HERE.

WE STRUGGLE AGAINST A TIDE OF DOUBT AND DESPERATION...

...CLINGING TO FLEETING ANSWERS, LIKE BITS OF WRECKAGE IN AN OCEAN WITHOUT A SHORE, LEST THE WATERS OF TIME TAKE US TO A PLACE WE DARE NOT VENTURE--

--DESPAIR.

THOSE ANSWERS WE FIND ARE, SO OFTEN, OBSCURED, MANIPULATED, AND DISTORTED INTO SOMETHING RECOGNIZABLE--

--A MERE OPIATE FOR THE SOUL.

BUT SOMETIMES...

"CULT" MY ASS.

NOPD Captain Slain In Cult Massacre.

...FRAGMENTS OF GREAT TRUTH REVEAL THEMSELVES--

--ONES SO POWERFUL THAT WE ALMOST DARE NOT BELIEVE IN THEM.

IN THE END, WE HAVE LITTLE ELSE...

# DEAD SOULS ARCHIVE

The following material appeared as a series of
supplementary offerings in the pages of the original
*Dead Souls* three-issue miniseries published by
Seraphemera Books from 2008-2010. The short
back-up story, "An Immortal Interlude," was published in the anthology of the *New Orleans Drink n'
Draw Society: Free Comic Book Day May 4, 2013*.
The narrative captions have been modified to reflect
the style of *Dead Souls: Resurrection*, wherein a painting of the speaker is attached to the first instance of
the monologue. Otherwise, it should be considered
in continuity, and a brief glimpse at Vlad, Erzsébet,
and St. Germain's journey to Russia.

# DEAD SOULS
AN IMMORTAL INTERLUDE OR MARY'S BLOOD MEASURE

**ERZSÉBET BÀTHORY!** THE AMARANTHINE COUNTESS WITH A TASTE FOR *TORTURE!*

**VLAD DRACULA!** THE UNDYING PRINCE WHO FIGHTS EVIL... WITH *MURDER!*

**ST. GERMAIN!** THE KEEPER OF THE PHILOSOPHER'S STONE WHO COMBATS IMMORTAL *DEPRAVITY!*

BECAUSE YOU DEMANDED IT! THEY'RE BACK!

OUR FLIGHT FROM NEW ORLEANS TO RUSSIA WAS OFTEN DELAYED. THOUGH WE COULD NOT DIE, ST. GERMAIN STILL REQUIRED TIME TO PLAN HIS NEXT MOVE.

WE SHOULDN'T HAVE TO GET OFF U.S. SOIL SO FUCKING QUICKLY, BUT--

I WILL NOT KILL POLICE OFFICERS FOR YOU.

NOT THE DRACULA I READ ABOUT, MATE.

I HAD RESIGNED MYSELF TO ASSISTING HIM, DESPITE MY BETTER JUDGMENT. IT GAVE ME A PURPOSE. BUT, ERZSEBET HAD GROWN RESTLESS.

YOU'D ALREADY KILLED EVERYONE ELSE IN THE--

I AM LEAVING. I NEED TO GET OUT OF THIS ROOM.

"DON'T BE LONG. WE'RE LEAVING IN THE MORNING."

ARROGANT ENGLISH BASTARD THINKS HE CAN TELL ME--

VROOM

WHUMP!

FUCK!!!

JESUS, ARE YOU OKAY?!

FUCKING CAR JUST CAME OUT OF NOWHERE...

YES, I AM FINE. IT IS NOT AS BAD AS IT--

MY GOD, WHAT HAPPENED HERE?

HER NAME WAS ANGIE. SHE HANGED HERSELF. SORRY, UM, I'M FOX. WHAT'S YOUR NAME?

I GUESS YOU WOULD CALL ME "ELIZABETH" IN ENGLISH. I AM...*VISITING* FROM HUNGARY.

THAT'S COOL.

LOOK, IT WAS A LONG TIME COMING. PEOPLE PICKED ON HER--LIKE, A LOT.

WHY?

JUST--SHE WAS, YOU KNOW, ONE OF THE "OUT" KIDS. HER FAMILY WAS POOR. SHE HAD ACNE. DOESN'T MATTER.

THERE'S THIS GIRL JACKIE. SHE'S KIND OF THE QUEEN BEE AROUND HERE. IT'S HER AND THOSE CUNTS THAT FOLLOW HER AROUND.

THEY DROVE HER TO IT. THEY ASKED HER TO COME TO THIS PARTY AND THEN FUCKING SPIT ON HER INVITATION AND THREW IT AT HER.

MAY I HAVE THAT?

SURE. WELCOME TO HOBOKEN.

LATER...

IT'S A OUIJA BOARD. YOU, LIKE, USE IT TO TALK TO GHOSTS. SUPPOSEDLY, THEY, YOU KNOW, HEAR YOU AND ANSWER.

DOES IT REALLY WORK?

WE SHOULD USE IT TO TALK TO ANGIE!

AND DO WHAT? MAKE FUN OF HER GROSS FUCKING PIMPLES IN THE AFTERLIFE?

SHE DESERVED IT. I HOPE SHE'S ROTTING IN HELL.

HA! OH GOD, THAT IS SO FUCKED UP, JACKIE.

HEY, HAVE ANY OF YOU EVER HEARD OF BLOODY MARY?

WHAT? LIKE THAT THING YOU DO IN THE BATHROOM? IN THE MIRROR?

# HISTORICAL ATROCITIES AND MORBID FASCINATIONS: AN INTERVIEW WITH DANI FILTH

## BY KURT AMACKER

*Dani Filth sings for the Grammy-nominated British extreme metal group, Cradle of Filth. Their 1998 album* Cruelty and the Beast *presents the story of Elizabeth Bathory\* as an epic rock opera. The band is often credited with introducing the Countess to the modern Gothic and metal subcultures.*

**Kurt:** You've said before that you first encountered Elizabeth Bathory in school, reading books on vampire folklore and the Hammer horror film *Countess Dracula*. But from where does your fascination with her come? Do you see her as just a historical horror show, or is there something more involving at play?

**Dani:** I guess it does go a little bit more than just a horror show. The fascination with her obviously led us to do the

*\*For the duration of the interview, the Anglicized version of the Countess's name will be used.*

*Cruelty and the Beast* album, and that was a notable feat, completing it entirely. It was a huge project, trying to weave it to music. During that period, I became kind of integrated with everything about her personality. And, as undeniably good as it may sound, I kind of felt a connection to what went on. There wasn't an admiration or anything like that. But there was definitely a found connection with the story—with the supposed story—a morbid fascination, at first, that grew into something a bit more.

**Kurt:** You say the "supposed story." There's a great deal of controversy over the nature and extent of her crimes. You know that most historians dismiss the blood-bathing thing. Some of them say that maybe she didn't kill as many as has been reported, or perhaps there was some conspiracy by the Hungarian crown to imprison her.

**Dani:** The blood-bath thing is almost as ridiculous as the idea that Dracula impaled whole armies of peo-ple—you'd need another army about six times the size to do that! These things have become greatly exaggerated over the years. Obviously, those are the most enduring images, as Dracula and Eliza-beth have become icons and fairy tales. The blood-bath is obviously the first thing that you're going to think of in association with Elizabeth Bathory. The Todd McFarlane figure of her depicts her in the infamous bath. The first time that I read about her, that was the thing that was attributed to her—the fact that she bathed in the blood of virgins. It's all a bit of hokum, really.

**Kurt:** What do you think that an artistic depiction like *Cruelty and the Beast* or the movie *Countess Dracula* owes to history? We know that a lot of her crimes have been exaggerated, but these are works that revel in those stories.

**Dani:** It's an artistic depiction. It's everything that tends to the fairy tale—anything that has been exaggerated or has cemented itself over the years. The Todd McFarlane figure wouldn't have been quite as impressive had she not been reveling in a bath of virgins' blood. It's the same about McFarlane's Dracu-la toy. If he wasn't in the midst of impal-ing some poor hapless Turk assassin or something, it wouldn't have been quite the same. It's those images you see if you go to a wax museum. They used to have an Elizabeth Bathory figure in the London Dungeon at one point—I think she's been moved to the York Dungeon or the Edinburgh Dungeon. That figure had the same thing—she was bathing in blood. I guess these are things that become iconic with the figures as horror

characters, just as Christopher Lee has become synonymous with Dracula, as much as he'd like to shun it. You get attached to the things that shine through in the legend—always the most maca-bre aspects.

**Kurt:** It's interesting, because people become almost disappointed when you point out that many of Dracula's and Elizabeth's crimes were likely not as horrible as books have made them out to be.

**Dani:** Undoubtedly, she was cruel. I dare say there was some cruelty involved, but who knows? Who could really tell you? Her legend wouldn't be half as fascinating, would it, if there were not some slight exaggeration?

**Kurt:** Now, because of that exaggera-tion, she's almost regarded as a "real life vampire" of sorts by some peo-ple—though she certainly wasn't in any traditional sense of the word.

**Dani:** Well, she was "vampirized" in Hammer's *Countess Dracula*—the movie from which we plucked Ingrid Pitt to our version of Elizabeth Bathory in *Cruelty and the Beast.* I think Tony Thorne wrote a book called *Countess Dracula* as well—which is sort of an attention-seeking title—in which he tries to undercut the myth and break through the legend. The book is very well-researched.

**Kurt:** I'll be interviewing him for the second issue of *Dead Souls*, as a matter of fact. He's actually seen Cradle of Filth play live. Now, I know you are acquainted with Dennis Báthory-Kitsz, who claims to be descended from Eliza-beth. He's a musician and he's writing an opera about the Countess. Have you encountered him or any other scholars closely associated with the more historical side of her story?

**Dani:** I first "met" Dennis on the Internet, where we exchanged e-mails over our infatuation with his descendant, which inevitably led to excited conversations about a tie between my band and his operas. One such flight of fancy would be playing *Cruelty and the Beast* at the ruins of Čachtice Castle in Slovakia, alongside performances of his opera about the Blood Countess. That would still be amazing. I met him once in the flesh, quite by a weird chance. We were playing a show in Montreal the same day he was visiting the city with his wife. By complete luck, he passed by the venue we were playing in and spoke to our manager, who then invited him to the show. Later that evening, I was introduced to him wearing a Bathory—the band—shirt that I'd just been given that day in a local rock store. It was a curious coincidence, for sure. We actually only lost contact due to my inefficiency in keeping in regular contact with anyone other than my wife and daughter. I'm shit like that, and my Mum's always moaning about it!

As for scholars, not really, but there's a

**The ruins of Čachtice Castle in Slovakia**

girl who's infatuated with us—I won't give her name away. At one point, she followed us around most of North America. She claimed that in a past life, she'd been Elizabeth Bathory. Strangely enough, I'd been her husband. That was a coincidence, wasn't it? I thought she was a bit kooky. Other than that, there's Gavin Baddeley, who has cowritten my book, *The Gospel of Filth*. He's done some research on her, which obviously surfaces in the pages of our book in the chapter about *Cruelty and the Beast*. Ingrid Pitt is fascinated by her, and she wrote a book called *The Ingrid Pitt Book Of Murder, Torture And Depravity*, in which she touched upon the Countess.

**Kurt:** How do you, personally, negotiate the line between fascination and admiration with someone like Elizabeth? *Cruelty and the Beast* and the song "Dusk and Her Embrace" both express an intense interest in her, but they almost cross the line into admiration. This is something I personally struggle with. I have a painting of her on the wall of my dining room, but I don't approve of her actions. It seems like we walk the line between what interests us and what we admire in these cases. Is that something that you struggle with?

**Dani:** Yes, it is. We're working on an album about Gilles des Rais, and he was more notably disturbing and not as initially alluring as the Countess. He was male, he was warlike and thuggish, and his crimes were against children. But you do find yourself encapsulated by the history while trying to turn it into a story that will fascinate others without, like you said, crossing that line into admiration. Admiration is a bit of a strong sentiment for a person of his caliber. I've got some serial killer artwork at home, and I find it fascinating. But they're not on major display in my upstairs. I tend to ask myself the same question—that if the victims were to see these, how it would look from their viewpoint, and how it could be a horribly ugly thing to own. At the same time, my interest gets the better of me. I really do have quite a deep-reaching morbid fascination. I like the fairytale aspect of it, as well. I like things being made palatable in that way. I've always been interested in the dark arts and the occult. I grew up on it.

My daughter's just done a part on our album about Gilles des Rais as one of the victims. Some people might say, "Oh, that's quite controversial in the fact that it's about a child killer. There you are writing an album about him, and you put your own daughter on it." Some people might say that's kind of morbid. But I think that we should explore our fears. I'm a very happy-go-lucky kind of person. I love life. But I still have this very deep-rooted interest in the macabre, and the morbid, and death. That is where I find my life. And some people don't really understand that.

**Kurt:** Are there any plans to revisit the Countess in any of your future works, or do you think that Cradle of Filth has moved on?

**Dani:** There was the thought about revisiting the *Cruelty and the Beast* album at the castle, but I think we've done pretty much as much we could, set within the historical time frame, which is why we decided to explore someone else—the Gilles des Rais story—on this next record. I don't think we can possi-

bly do anything more. But, now, your comic has brought her out of her own time and into a modern setting, and I'm really looking forward to the second one.

**Kurt:** Thank you, Dani. It's been a pleasure.

*Cradle of Filth's new album is scheduled for release in October, alongside Dani Filth's book with Gavin Baddeley,* The Gospel of Filth. *Much thanks go to Dani for his time and consideration. This interview would not have happened were it not for the hard work of Amy Sciarretto at Roadrunner Records, who arranged the conversation.*

\*\*\*

Dead Souls #2 *will be released in October of this year. Please visit us online at www.myspace.com/deadsoulsnola.*

*T-shirts, stickers, and copies of this comic can be ordered at www.seraphemera.org.*

*Questions, comments, and letters should be directed to deadsouls@seraphemera.org. Any correspondence may be reprinted with the author's reply in future issues.*

# ELIZABETH BATHORY IN HISTORY AND LEGEND: AN INTERVIEW WITH TONY THORNE

## BY KURT AMACKER

*Tony Thorne is the Language and Innovation Consultant to King's College London, of the University of London. In 1997, he released the definitive English-language biography of Elizabeth Bathory\*, Countess Dracula, which is currently out of print.*

**Kurt:** A lot of your recent work has been on linguistics. And, yet, you wrote *The Blood Countess* in 1997, which is probably the best English-language work about Elizabeth Bathory ever written.

**Tony:** You're right, that was kind of a slight departure. I started out doing language and linguistic books. During the late 1980s when the Communist countries in Eastern Europe were first opening up, the whole culture of the region was pretty much unknown in the

UK and the US. At the time, there was very little published about its history. Most Western scholars just don't have a command of those languages, and I do. There was a whole literature and a whole history that I felt needed to be opened up. I later went on to write *Children of the Night*, which is a non-fiction book about vampires. A lot of the research for that was done in Eastern Europe.

**Kurt:** Your work was a help in researching Elizabeth Bathory in *Dead Souls*, because some of those primary source materials had never been published in English.

**Tony:** A lot of it is still not available in English. It means that you can get people like Valentine Penrose, who wrote *The Bloody Countess*. You can just make it up quite romantically because the sources are just not available and accessible. It was interesting, because it was just kind of virgin territory in a way—if that's not the wrong word to use. Unfortunately, now there's a small kind of industry going, just as there is with Bram Stoker. There are people who have tried to make a career out of Bathory, but they're not particularly scholarly. I was surprised that *Children of the Night* didn't sell better. It does seem that people want to read fiction and fantasy. That's fine, but they don't want necessarily to find out the truth. Fictional vampire books still sell better than factual ones. It's a pity, from my point of view.

**Kurt:** I think the problem is that people don't distinguish between the separate roles each play. When I interviewed Dani Filth, the singer of Cradle of Filth, for the first issue of *Dead Souls*, he readily admitted that the story about Bathory bathing in blood wasn't true. He emphasized that one story tends to the fairy tale and another to the history.

**Tony:** That's fine by me. But, I still think the facts are very interesting!

**Kurt:** People don't like having their fairy tales shot down. The idea that there was this woman that bathed in blood to stay young is thrilling. When you take all that away and look at the facts, they're still very interesting in their own right, but they're not what people have grown up with.

**Tony:** I don't want to take that away from them. To go to the other extreme, I met some very interesting people when I was researching—people who really were into the fantasy—people who do drink blood and who take it very seriously. Some of them are even intel-

lectuals. I met a doctor from Berlin who was into blood-drinking and various artists from Holland and elsewhere who were really into vampire rituals. I don't mean in a kind of campy way. I mean in a very occult sense. Vampirism and blood-drinking were part of it. There's a whole range of people out there getting involved in these things.

**Kurt:** For my part, I'm really grateful for the work you did on *Countess Dracula*. It's a really illuminating look at the subject. There haven't been many works like it.

**Tony:** The story isn't finished and the research isn't over. I'm still convinced that there are more papers in the archives in Hungary, the Ukraine, Poland, and Slovakia that I haven't been able to identify yet. There are private libraries and public records that haven't been opened up, along with church archives. I'm hoping to have an opportunity, but I haven't right now. But there are some Hungarian and Slovak scholars who are working on it. A friend of mine is preparing a kind of scholarly book in Hungarian about Bathory, and I'm hoping he may discover some new papers because he's very good in the archives. Maybe one day we'll find out some more opinions from her contemporaries, because there's a deafening silence. People must have talked about her after she was condemned, but there's virtually nothing in the records. She just disappeared.

**Kurt:** What about the possibility of her journal being in the state archives in Hungary? Is that just a legend?

**Tony:** It's a legend. It's possible that she did keep a journal, but it's unlikely.

French and English noblewomen at that time often did keep journals—not all of them, but the educated ones did. But it wasn't common in Hungary. I really looked very hard in the records. We never found any evidence. Hungarian noblewomen were just too busy trying to control their possessions and keep order in the kingdom with the Turks at the door. It would be fantastic, but the people who say it exists—this is non-sense. No one has ever found it.

**Kurt**: It's like her gravesite. You hear different things from time to time.

**Tony:** Again, I think nobody's sure about that. I tried very hard to find out where she was buried. It's kind of infuriating. She could be under the church in Čachtice. I wanted permission to get into the crypt and it's really difficult. There's a lot of bureaucracy there and without influence, you just can't do these things. But it's also possible that she was buried in Poland or somewhere in Hungary. But, she was definitely buried. They wouldn't have thrown her body into a field or anything. Whatever she'd done, she was too important and too noble. There is a grave somewhere, but nobody has yet found it.

**Kurt:** Can you surmise your opinion on her guilt or innocence? I realize it's very complicated, and there was the possibility of a number of conspiracies —everything from the Hungarian crown over debts owed to her husband to familial conflicts. Can you concisely give your opinion on whether she was responsible for killing all of those girls?

**Tony:** I was criticized over this by some of the people I spoke to in my research for *Countess Dracula*. They said that I was kind of sitting on the fence and that I should come down on whether she was guilty or not. I'm sorry not to give you a straight answer, but it's actually really difficult. My opinion still veers from one side to the other, depending on which bits of research I'm looking at. I'll tell you what I think now. First of all, I did discover some important information, which isn't in the book, which I learned afterward. In the book, I claimed that the wife of György Thurzó [the Palatine of Hungary, later sent by the crown to arrest Bathory for her crimes] tried to enter her castle and take some of her jewelry and possessions This is wrong, and it is because of a wrong reading of a document. It wasn't Thurzó's wife, but Bathory's own daughter. There was definitely a conspiracy against her. Even her own daughters were trying to grab her wealth before she died, which by rights belonged to her son. That doesn't make her innocent. I'm now convinced that there were some spectacular cruelties and atrocities going on in her court. Whether she was really herself, with her own hands, torturing people—I just don't think we can prove it. With the way they kept records, you couldn't prove it by modern standards. But they could've accused her of witchcraft or adultery, and it would've been much easier. Other women were accused of those things all over Europe. They didn't, though. They accused her of extreme cruelty. When I wrote *Countess Dracula*, I was completely undecided of whether she'd been framed or was guilty. But I'm convinced now that these women in her court were torturing and abusing girls. I doubt it was 650 of them. This was a tradition—that you dressed up and exaggerated the evidence outrageously. That was standard practice. I'm sorry if that's kind of a weak version of the story that I'm putting forward.

**Kurt:** No worries. You're probably the best English-language authority in the world to consult on the subject.

**Tony:** I'm hoping that some Hungarian and Slovak scholars will study this further. They'd have much more access. But for the moment, my book is, in a way, the most authoritative because nothing else has been produced. But, I'm convinced that there was some truth. There must be a reason why they accused her of cruelty, because it would've been much easier to frame her in some other way. It's like there's no smoke without fire.

**Kurt:** What do you think about the more contemporary fascination with her in the Gothic and metal subcultures?

**Tony:** Some of the stuff that people write or believe about her is crazy and untrue. But she was an incredibly charismatic person. We've now created a mythical version, and I think she's a fascinating character. I think that the idea of a really sinister, glamorous, demonic woman is very powerful. And she has the virtue of really existing. This does give the myth a special resonance. I think she's an incredible persona, so I completely agree with people that get into her.

**Kurt:** It seems like the pop culture obsession with her has reached a fever pitch over the past few years. It's culminating with the release of two films about her. But it seems like she's always been on the minds of a lot of people in the Gothic and metal subcultures.

**Tony:** She has always been there...lurking in their consciousnesses.

**Kurt:** It's interesting that a historical subject like the Countess could work her way into popular culture, almost in the same way that a band or a film might.

**Tony:** It is pretty remarkable. It's a story that's hundreds of years old and it still grips people.

**Kurt:** Well, I do hope we hear more from you in the future. It's been a pleasure talking with you.

\*\*\*

*Much to our surprise, Alan Moore really liked the first issue of* Dead Souls. *That's about the highest praise a comic can receive, as far as we're concerned*

*All due apologies for the delay of this issue, but a hurricane or two complicated things. Regardless, the response to* Dead Souls #1 *has been above and beyond our wildest expectations. By the time you read this, we should even have national distribution through Haven.*

*T-shirts, stickers, and copies of this comic can be ordered online at www.seraphemera.org. The first issue is still available. Both comics can also be ordered at Amazon.com.*

*Questions, comments, and letters should be directed to deadsouls@seraphemera.org. Any correspondence may be reprinted with the author's reply in future issues.*

# No Rest for the Wicked

## By Kurt Amacker

This is the end of a very long road. I started writing what became *Dead Souls* in December of 2002, but didn't really start taking the project seriously until Fall of 2003. I was on medical hold at Camp Pendleton with the Marines after a knee injury kept me from going to Iraq with my battalion. I finally settled on Lou as the artist in December 2004. I shopped the book around at San Diego Comic-Con the next summer and realized that I had no idea what I was doing. It was only after a lot of trial and error that I learned how to passably letter a comic, let alone go through the hours of clean-up and post-production work that it's taken to make *Dead Souls* a reality. Even then, things didn't really take off until Spring of 2008, when I met Marc Moorash of Seraphemera Books at a friend's house in Houston and finally found a publisher willing to attach their name to this comic.

Ultimately, I began this project after listening to Cradle of Filth in college drove me to read and write again. I thought it was only appropriate to involve Dani Filth in the first issue. To my delight, he gave me a glowing cover quote and the interview you saw in issue one. *Dead Souls* even got a mention in *The Gospel of Filth*—a chronicle of the band's history and inspirations. I can't thank Dani enough for his continued support for this project and for keeping in touch even after the interview.

You might have noticed that Alan Moore offered us a very kind review on the cover of the second issue. I've been fortunate enough to stay in touch with Mr. Moore since I interviewed him for the release of *Lost Girls* in 2006. We'd talked on and off up until that point, and he agreed to give me a review. Frankly, I expected to be told to try again next time, but he liked *Dead Souls* quite a bit. That's probably the highest praise a comic can receive, and I almost still can't believe it. I've even double-checked since then, and he still likes it.

What started out as a sort of superhero comic by way of Cradle of Filth turned into a story about a man determined to rage at God's absence. In the Jean Paul Sartre play *No Exit*, the damned aren't tortured. They sit in a waiting room with each other. I liked the idea that the worst thing possible was utter meaninglessness. Vlad and Elizabeth aren't necessarily in hell, but they suffer the worst for their not understanding. They don't even have death to look forward to. Their questions might go on unanswered until the end of time and even beyond that. Really, their experience is just an extrapolation of our own. We come into this world not knowing where we came from, why we are here, or what the future holds. Our lives are clouded by uncertainty. Despite arguments appealing to faith or intuition, we don't know if God is real in the same way that we know other things. Our lives could very well just be mechanical exercises in survival and reproduction. But we don't even know that with certainty. We float through infinity, and only death answers the question by removing our ability to ask. Vlad, Elizabeth, and those like them have to keep asking forever.

So, what do you do? What do they do?

Elizabeth's hedonism as fundamentally hollow. They set out to destroy those that defy his personal morality. It's not a recommendable way to live, but the human condition is a dangerous one.

With *Mathilda* creator Tedd Walley at BSI Comics, Free Comic Book Day 2009

With Dani Filth in Atlanta, February 2009

Fight it. Find meaning somehow. Make it up if you have to. We all do this. We subscribe to religions and philosophies, or we settle for atheism—which even provides answers of a sort. Vlad and Elizabeth revert to violence, which was the one thing they knew best in life. Vlad's Nietzschean outlook drives him to aggressively reject his circumstances and try to reclaim them. He exposes

Only with St. Germain's guidance and Kierkegaardian approach to faith do Vlad and Elizabeth find a direction that doesn't involve killing anyone in their way. And St. Germain's path is misguided in its own right. It's not the "correct" answer. It just directs violence towards something arguably worse. Shades of grey abound, and we're brought to ask questions to which we'll never learn the answers. We all have to figure out how to survive on our own.

This is just the beginning. There will be sequels to *Dead Souls* and an eventual trade paperback, along with other comics. My thanks to all of you for the years of support and the limitless patience between issues. This has been a harrowing journey, but it has convinced me to continue to write comics. There are stories inside me that cry out to escape, and I intend to give them their due. Thank you all for believing.

# FURTHER ATROCITIES

Early super-fan Kendall Kinchen at the Mississippi Southern
Fried Comic Con in 2010, now singer of Sleep Juliette

Android Lust performing at the 2010 release party for
*Dead Souls #3* at the Hi-Ho Lounge in New Orleans

Posing with with DJ LostTwistedSoul (now DJ
BeauTato) with the third issue, at the release party

Models Jessica Kendall and TheJadeRose posing for our
ill-fated Kickstarter in 2014. Credits: Glam Trash Rebel
Photography and Mark KwiatKowski. Used with permission.

A very small selection of the many
photos of *Dead Souls* fans and signings
from over the years. Thank you to
everyone for your endless patience. I can
only hope that *Dead Souls: Resurrection*
has been worth the wait.

Visiting the Bathory castle in Čhactice, Slovakia in
2015 (finally)

# THE CREATORS

Kurt Amacker is a comic book writer from New Orleans, Louisiana. He graduated from Loyola University in 2002 and received his Master's degrees from Tulane University in 2017 and 2019. He began writing his first miniseries, *Dead Souls*, while recovering from an injury in the United States Marine Corps. After the first issue was published in 2008, he continued writing comics while DJing in the raucous French Quarter Goth scene. His work has been publicly praised by Alan Moore, Hart Fisher, Jyrki 69, Victor Gischler, and, of course, Dani Filth. His first prose novel, *Bloody October*, was published in 2016.

He continues to live in New Orleans with his wife, Sabrina, and their black cats, Vlad and Erzsébet.

Monty Borror is an illustrator/author whose previous works include *Quarantined* from AAM/Markosia as well as *Garbage Day* and *Spirit Window* from Arcana, along with various short stories from several other publishers. His scripts and prose short stories have been published by many small press publishers in the United States. *Cold Blooded Chillers*, from Heske Horror, in which Borror's work appears, was the winner of the Bronze Independent Publisher's Award in 2009. He was also a finalist in The L. Ron Hubbard Illustrators of the Future contest in 2001 yet remains Scientology free. He pencilled and inked *Cradle of Filth: The Curse of Venus Aversa* for Dark Notes Press in 2014.

Dark Notes Press, LLC is based in New Orleans, Louisiana. The company offers a line of graphic novels and prose that emphasizes the integral connections between literature and music.

Dark Notes Press. Words That Rock.

DARK NOTES PRESS